# Xylophone Music from Ghana

**Trevor Wiggins**

**and**

**Joseph Kobom**

*White Cliffs Media Company*

*Crown Point, IN*

White Cliffs Media Company
P.O. Box 561
Crown Point, IN 46307

Distributed to the book trade by
The Talman Company.

Revised edition of a book previously published by Bretton Press.

Printed on acid-free paper in the United States of America.

**Library of Congress Cataloging in Publication Data**

Wiggins, Trevor, 1953–
    Xylophone music from Ghana / Trevor Wiggins and Joseph Kobom.
       p.  cm.   — (Performance in world music series ; no. 6)
    ISBN 0-941677-30-3 (paper)
    ISBN 0-941677-36-2 (spiral)
    1. Xylophone. 2. Xylophone music—history and criticism. 3. Folk music—Ghana—History and criticism. 4. Xylophone—Instruction and study.  I. Kobom, Joseph. II. Title.  III. Series
    ML1048.W53  1992
    786.8'43'09667—dc20                    92-3212
                                          CIP
                                          MN

# Contents

### Introduction
The xylophone (*gyil*) in Ghana is played mainly in the Upper West region of the country by people speaking the Dagaare and Sisaala languages.

### Building a Xylophone
Building a xylophone is a specialized undertaking and players do not normally make their own instruments.

### Performance
The player sits on a low stool, or anything else convenient such as a block of wood or stone, with the lowest bars to the player's left.

### Using Ghanaian Pentatonic Xylophone Music in Education
There is considerable interest in the contribution world musics are able to make to a broad based view of music in education, widening pupil's musical and social horizons. Children make the most sense of unfamiliar music when they are able to play it. A simple Time Unit Box Sytem numbering method for learning the music is presented, along with traditional music notation.

### Transcriptions of Xylophone Music
The transcriptions show what was taught by Joseph Kobom. The basic patterns have a number of fairly standard variations which may differ in detail between performances.

# Chapter One

## Introduction

The xylophone (*gyil*) in Ghana is played mainly in the Upper West region of the country by people speaking the Dagaare and Sisaala languages, whose territory also extends into Burkina Faso.

The information and music presented in this book was provided by Joseph Kobom who learned to play the xylophone in his home town of Nandom in Northern Ghana, and who is now an instructor at the School of Performing Arts, University of Ghana. The xylophone and its music have become widely known throughout Ghana, partly as a result of a short extract of xylophone music played by Joseph Kobom being used as the signature tune for Ghana Television. As a result, Joseph, who now lives in the Nima area of Accra, is much in demand to play at hotels where he may share the bill with a highlife (African hybrid dance music) band.

In some areas the instrument is considered to be sacred and is played only for funerals. However in the Wa district the xylophone is not played for funerals and in the central (Jirapa) area xylophones are frequently used for all kinds of musical occasions. The most common type of recreational music used for dancing is called "Bawa" and is usually an elaboration of a song tune. Funeral music is frequently referred to as "Lobi" xylophone music and is played to announce a death. Music may also be played to encourage mourning at a funeral, and the xylophone is also used for some cult dances.

Xylophone players each have their own individual style which they gradually develop by imitating and adapting the music of other players. Experienced players have their own individual "signature tune" which they have composed and with which they introduce their performances. A master xylophonist is able to improvise on anything he hears and will be imitated in turn. The styles of great players can be recognised instantly, mainly by the strength and style of their left hand. Sometimes players will reverse the xylophone, performing with the lower notes to the right — a practice involving some risk and needing strong spiritual protection. Joseph Kobom suggests that this style has been learned from players in the neighboring country of Burkina Faso.

Joseph Kobom

## Joseph Kobom

Joseph Kobom narrates how his wish to play the xylophone was apparent from an early age. As a baby he clenched his fists as though playing the xylophone so small beaters were soon put into his hands. He learned to play in the traditional way by imitating other performers rather than having formal instruction. Practice is sometimes done using a pit xylophone, in which the bars are strung together as usual, but suspended on a grass frame over an earth pit which acts as a resonator. The xylophone can be played as a solo instrument, but is also frequently played as a duet with the less experienced player taking a lower supporting part. Playing the xylophone is considered to be a dangerous undertaking spiritually, so the first money that is earned by a young player is used to prepare appropriate defenses or charms, some of which are suspended beneath the third lowest bar of the instrument.

Traditions and Legends

There are a number of traditions associated with the xylophone. In Ghana it is played only by men. In playing the xylophone the player's left hand is very important as it generally acts as a steady timekeeper for the improvisations and syncopations of the right hand. To threaten to injure the player's left hand is therefore extremely serious. Players will also strengthen their left hand by using it for actions normally done only by the right hand, such as eating food. The Dagaare people have a legend telling how they acquired the xylophone:

> *A man was walking in the bush when he heard a fairy playing the xylophone. He was so fascinated by the music that he went home and called his friends to make preparations to go and catch the fairy. He knew it would be difficult as the fairy could only be controlled by people with special powers, not just ordinary men. The man went back into the bush with his friends and because he was so brave and strong he was able to capture the fairy. He then threatened to kill the fairy unless it showed him everything about making and playing a xylophone. The fairy told him he must first make a strong medicine using certain leaves. Next he must collect certain sticks, break them, then carve them (to make the bars). He must also find a special long calabash which grew by the river, cut it and put it into water until the inside rotted, then hollow it out (to make the resonators). The man did everything he was told and gradually he learned all the secrets of making and playing a xylophone. The man then took an axe and killed the fairy and built a fire to roast the meat which he ate with his friends. When they took the xylophone home and started playing it the women were completely mystified by the music until the men told them to dance to it. But in spite of roasting the fairy, its blood remained part of the instrument, so the xylophone cannot be played by women because they menstruate and their blood would not mix with that of the fairy.*

If a woman were to play the xylophone, acording to Dagaare myth, she would become unable to bear children. This legend illustrates well how closely connected are music, myth and social organisation within a culture.

## Learning to Play the Xylophone

I have been a lecturer at Bretton Hall College in West Yorkshire, England and I currently teach at Dartington College of the Arts in Devon, England. My long-standing interest in African music led to an exchange program with the University of Ghana. During a full program of teaching and studying, I received lessons in the playing of the traditional Ghanaian xylophone (*gyil*) from Joseph Kobom.

Ghanaians are proud of their xylophones and pleased when other people make a good attempt to play the music. I once sat playing at the side of a road in Accra for 30 minutes while waiting for a lift and received almost non-stop cheering and clapping from passing minibuses! In modern settings outside of Ghana, xylophone music may be played and enjoyed by all, men and women alike. I hope this book will help you, the reader, to appreciate and perform this enjoyable and engaging music from an African culture.

# Chapter Two

## Building a Xylophone

**B**uilding a xylophone is a specialized undertaking and players do not normally make their own instruments, although the maker will usually be a very competent player.

A xylophone builder will need a good understanding of practical acoustics and woodworking. One builder I interviewed told me the methods used include firing the wood for the bars and shaping, tempering and boosting up the sound quality of the bars. This process ensures the uniform vibration of the keys, adjusts the resonating frequency of the gourds, and enriches the tone of the instrument by adjusting the "singing" of the spider's membranes covering the holes in the gourds.

The tree from which the bars are traditionally made (usually a type of mahogany) is thought to be spiritually dangerous, requiring a black hen to be sacrificed and a prayer to be said a few days before the tree is felled. Sometimes the tree roots are cut and the tree is left until it falls. The wood should be left for some 6–7 years to dry out and become seasoned. A different wood is used for the frame of the instrument; less hard and more flexible, it is frequently found near rivers and is not considered to have the same power as the tree for the bars.

Once the wood has seasoned, the bars are roughly cut to size, then suspended over a pit for tuning. This is done in the same way as for all instruments with bars, removing wood from the back of the center of the bar to lower the pitch, and from the underside of the ends to raise it. For a 14-bar xylophone, they range in size from about 61cm long by 7cm wide for the lowest bar, to 44cm long by 4cm wide for the highest. The scale it is tuned to is anhemipentatonic, that is, it has five notes to the "octave" with no semitones, and does not fit into western tempered tuning. The relative tuning has a tendency towards equalizing the intervals compared with the western pentatonic scale, thus the "whole tones" tend to be larger, while the "minor thirds" are smaller. This means that there is often no specific pitch at which a

5

Relative size and graduation of xylophone bars.

Resonating gourds with spider's egg case to provide buzz.

piece of music must be begun; the performer will decide where to start after playing a few notes to test the pitch of a new instrument, although music will generally be played at the same pitch on a known instrument.

There are different sizes of xylophone, some having 12 bars, others 14 or sometimes 17, as well as some bass versions of the instrument. There is not an absolute standard of pitch for xylophones, but the relative tuning of the bars is consistent. Most makers will set the pitch of an instrument either from aural memory, or by reference to a known xylophone. In fact the absolute pitch, at least for 14 bar xylophones, seems to be remarkably consistent with the pitch used by Joseph Kobom. Kobom's instrument matches very closely the pitch of a xylophone which I bought independently. Resonating gourds with spider's egg cases are added to provide "buzz."

When the bars have been selected and tuned to the appropriate pitches they are tied together with a thin "string" of antelope hide which has been dried and softened, usually with shea butter (a fat extracted from shea nuts). The bars and string must be treated with shea butter from time to time to stop them from drying out or cracking.

A number of gourds are now tested to find those which resonate the pitched bars the best. The gourds vary considerably in size, ranging from about 7cm to 15cm in maximum diameter, the smaller ones being roughly spherical, while the larger are more bottle shaped, with the bottom part much larger than the top. These then have usually two holes of approximately 15mm diameter drilled in them at the fullest part or the gourd which will later be covered with spider's egg case to provide the characteristic buzz of the instrument. The egg cases are often found in houses, usually in the kitchen, and have a texture not unlike cigarette paper, but considerably stronger. They are stuck over the holes in the gourds (frequently with saliva), and must be slightly slack if they are to buzz well. According to Joseph Kobom, not every bar should buzz loudly, otherwise there is the risk that the tone of the instrument will be obscured.

The xylophone frame is quite light in construction and is held together with strips of cowhide, often with other hide strips used for decoration. The dimensions of the frame match the changing size of the bars, varying from 34cm to 24cm in width, the length being 96cm. The key-bed is cushioned with hide and slopes downward in a curve from the lowest bar to the highest, being about 40cm high at the lowest bar, and 18cm at the highest. In performance the strings supporting the bars are generally pulled quite tight so that the bars are lifted almost clear of the key-bed to improve the resonance. The gourds are suspended beneath the bars in two rows, resonating alternate notes, in order to accommodate their size within the frame.

The wood for the beaters is about 30cm long and some 2–3cm in diameter. Traditionally the heads are made from thin strips of latex wound round the end and held together with glue to a diameter of 4–5cm. The modern version has a circle cut from car tire as the head, and is more durable, as the glue on the traditional beaters tends to soften and become sticky when the temperature rises.

Traditionally made xylophones can difficult to procure but may be worth the effort for those dedicated to the instrument. Modern xylophones may be substituted to good effect, especially those which are tuned to a pentatonic scale.

# Chapter Three

## Performance

The player sits on a low stool, or anything else convenient such as a block of wood or stone, with the lowest bars to the player's left, although as was mentioned earlier, they are sometimes reversed.

The beaters are held between the first and second fingers of each hand. This can be uncomfortable at first given the size of the sticks, and the professional player will develop considerable calluses on these two fingers. This grip, however, holds the beaters extremely firm in a straight line with the arm and helps to achieve the accuracy and force needed with such large and quite weighty beaters. The weight of the beaters means that the player needs to develop great strength in the wrists as the bars are hit with considerable force when playing loudly.

Xylophones can be played as solo instruments, but are also frequently played in pairs. When played as a pair the two instruments should be tuned the same, but one, the "female" instrument played by the leader, should have a slightly sharper tone than the "male" instrument of the accompanying player. The two players sit facing each other a short distance apart. The leader will decide which pieces are to be played and will begin to play the basic pattern, the other player then joining with a more repetitive accompanying figure. An example of a typical accompaniment figure can be seen in the "Bass part" of the transcription of *Tomeyielu*.

The start of a performance of each piece of music, or section within a particular style, tends to be fairly standard, partly so that it can be identified by other performers and the song established in the case of recreational music. There are also a number of stock rhythmic and melodic figurations which function as a pattern for further elaboration and improvisation by the skilled performer. The order of the variations and the length of the piece depends on the performer and the occasion — a return to the style of the beginning is

Playing position.

Holding the beaters.

frequently a signal that the piece is about to end. Most of the variation is in the right hand part while the left hand keeps an ostinato pattern, but it is the mark of an expert player to be able to combine this with more difficult interlocking or imitative variations in the left hand part as can be seen in *Kolaperbir*. The accompanying player is allowed some license in varying the pattern in response to the leader, but is expected to enhance rather than obscure the leader's playing! The leader can also introduce variations of dynamics which must be followed, and may link directly into another piece without stopping.

Performances often take place out of doors; with its "built-in" resonance from the gourds the instrument does not really benefit from the added reverberation of a building. The sound of the instrument carries well and can frequently be heard during the evening in Nima, mingled with the smell of wood or charcoal burners from street food sellers, as local xylophone makers play for their own pleasure.

Before commencing any pieces the player will test the sound and pitch of the instrument in order to establish its range, and which note will be used as the "tonic." This often involves playing a pattern of alternate notes from low to high and back (1–3–2–4–3–5 etc.) followed by a pattern of octaves. Players seem to remember the physical pattern of the notes rather than the pitches, and will decide to start a piece beginning on a different note on different instruments. The ease with which they do this is more remarkable considering that there are no convenient marks on the bars, or a pattern of black and white notes as an aid to location. With my Western training I found this difficult as I remembered the pieces by pitch rather than pattern. To Western ears, starting on a different note may give the same piece of music quite a different sound even though the pattern of notes is the same. While playing a performer will also usually sing if playing a recreational piece, sometimes altering the words of a song to praise listeners or friends in an appropriate manner, or make nasal/throaty noises as an aid to concentration or to express feeling.

# Chapter Four

## Using Ghanaian Pentatonic Xylophone Music in Education

With good reason, there is a great deal of pentatonic music used in music education. There is also considerable interest in the contribution that world musics are able to make to a broad based view of music in education, widening pupils' musical and and social horizons.

*Xylophone Music from Ghana* has all the advantages of being pentatonic in pitch, but its use of rhythm is in a style unfamiliar to most children. Children make the most sense of unfamiliar music when they are able to play it, or produce similar sounds themselves, which then help them to make more sense of the "authentic" performances they hear. I personally find this music very attractive to listen to, but even more fun to play, and I have had the same sentiments expressed by a number of friends and colleagues.

It is possible, with some loss of character, to play all these pieces on conventional western instruments. In the case of school instruments some adaptation may be necessary as many educational xylophones have a range of only 1½ octaves C-G. The left and right hand parts of most pieces could be split to make two separate interlocking parts which would recreate the music quite well if the left hand part was allocated to an instrument pitched an octave lower than the right hand part, and the limited compass would generally be adequate for each part.

The structure of the pieces is such that once the basic pattern is learned, there is scope and stimulation for creative variations by pupils. In a piece such as *Bobodgilaso tingnebanena* the first and third bars use the same three notes in each part: simple variations might use these in any order while retaining the quarter note pulse, then begin to experiment with adding rhythmic variation as can be seen and heard in the actual piece. *Kpanlogo* could begin as a game on one xylophone where one pupil plays the lower ostinato part and the other explors the effect of playing different notes in the gaps (before being taught the piece at all), thus extending creative as well as rhythmic ability. In any case, I would consider that there are strong arguments for teaching this music, and certainly the basic patterns, aurally in the first instance. This is the traditional way it would be taught in Ghana, and was the way I was taught by Joseph Kobom. It meant that I learned the music first, then considered how to write it in order to help me remember a number of pieces in a short time.

With some younger or less able pupils, the basic patterns may be quite difficult, so I have written out three pieces (*Derkpee, Kpanlogo, Tomeyielu*) in simplified versions in both regular music notation and in TUBS notation (see below). These gradually introduce the complexities of the original piece in a controlled way. Any music teacher could doubtless adapt the other pieces presented in the next chapter in the same way, suiting them to the ability of the pupils they teach. Most of the pieces, if they are played as two separate parts, have an upper part which is more complex rhythmically and technically than the lower part, and can thus accommodate differing abilities. In a number of pieces the basic patterns could also be played with pupils taking alternate bars e.g. *Kolaperbir, Kpanlogo*, then introducing variations within just one bar. For anyone familiar with Ghanaian traditional music, the xylophone pieces can also be combined with drum and bell timekeeping patterns, [How is the reader supposed to know these? There are many different bell patterns. Which one goes with which piece? — LWS] or you can use your imagination and develop the cross-rhythms already present in almost every piece.

## TUBS

Following the staff notation the same pieces are presented in the same order using TUBS (Time Unit Box System) notation. The name is probably more difficult than the actual notation which is probably easier to work out than staff notation if you are not a fluent reader of music. It is also better than staff notation in many ways for this music: it does not specify precise Western pitches, nor make an arbitrary decision about whether a note should be written as a short note plus a rest, or a longer note (unless you stop the sound, when you hit a xylophone bar it dies away at the same rate), and there are no bar-lines to divide the music into possibly inappropriate chunks or suggest an accent where none should be. TUBS notation works by starting with a very fast pulse, equal to the speed of the shortest note. A note to be played can then be indicated using a letter or number, with a dot to show when nothing is to be played on that pulse. As an example, the first part of the tune for "My country 'tis of thee" might look like this:

| C | . | C | . | D | . | B | . | . | C | D | . | E | . | E | . | F | . | E | . | . | D | C | . | D | . | C | . | B | . | C |

In the case of the xylophone music, the TUBS notation uses the numbers 1 – 5 to indicate different bars of the pentatonic scale. Like the Ghanaian players, you could decide for yourself which bar you will call "1." The staff notation uses $1 = C, 2 = D, 3 = E, 4 = G, 5 = A$, but I have used numbers rather than letters because the pitches of the Ghanaian instrument do not coincide exactly with the western notes. A line above the number is then used to indicate the upper octave and a line below, the lower, so the full range of the instrument is as follows, although the top two notes are not used in any transcription:

$$2\underline{3}\underline{4}\underline{5}\,1\,2\,3\,4\,5\,\overline{1}\,\overline{2}\,\overline{3}\,\overline{4}\,\overline{5}$$

Crosses are used to indicate a rhythm played with the wooden handle of the xylophone beater on the top bar of the instrument.

In notating xylophone music with two parts TUBS notation assigns the top line to the upper (right hand) part. The sign :| means that a section can be repeated as often as required. This applies to most sections, but occasionaly there is a link section between two parts of a piece which should not be repeated and this has only the line | at the end.

# Simple Derkpee

# Simple Kpanlogo

# Simple Tomeyielu

**17**

**21**

**25**

**29**

## SIMPLE DERKPEE

```
. | 1̄ | . | . | 5 | . | 5 | . | 5 | . | 5 | . | . | 5 | . | . | 4 | . | 1̄ | . | 1̄ | . | 1̄ | . | :|
4 | . | . | . | 3 | . | 3 | . | 3 | 3 | 3 | . | 3 | . | . | . | 3 | . | 4 | . | 4 | 4 | 4 | . | :|


. | 1̄ | 1̄ | . | 5 | . | 5 | . | 5 | . | 5 | . | . | 5 | 5 | . | 4 | . | 1̄ | . | 1̄ | . | 1̄ | . | :|
4 | . | . | . | 3 | . | 3 | . | 3 | 3 | 3 | . | 3 | . | . | . | 3 | . | 4 | . | 4 | 4 | 4 | . | :|


. | 1̄ | 1̄ | . | 5 | . | 5 | . | 5 | . | 5 | . | . | 5 | 5 | . | 4 | . | 1̄ | . | 1̄ | . | 1̄ | . | :|
4 | . | . | 3 | 3 | . | 3 | . | 3 | 3 | . | . | 3 | . | . | 3 | 3 | . | 4 | . | 4 | 4 | . | . | :|


. | 1̄ | . | . | 5 | . | 5 | . | 5 | . | 5 | . | . | 5 | . | . | 4 | . | 1̄ | . | 1̄ | . | 1̄ | . | :|
4 | . | . | 3 | . | . | 3 | . | . | 3 | . | . | 3 | . | . | 3 | . | . | 4 | . | . | 4 | . | . | :|


. | 1̄ | . | . | 5 | . | 5̲ | . | 5̲ | . | 5̲ | . | . | 5 | . | . | 4 | . | 1 | . | 1 | . | 1 | . | :|
4 | . | . | 3 | . | . | 3̲ | . | . | 3̲ | . | . | 3 | . | . | 3 | . | . | 4̲ | . | . | 4̲ | . | . | :|
```

## SIMPLE KPANLOGO

**System 1**

```
5 . . . . . 5 . . . 5 . 1̄ . 5 . 5 . . . . . 5 . 2̄ . 5 . 2̄ . 5 .
3 . . . 3 . . . 3 . . . 3 . . . 2 . . . 2 . . . 2 . . . 2 . . .
```

**System 2**

```
3 . 5 . . . 5 . . . 5 . 1̄ . 5 . . . . 5 . . 5 . 2̄ . 2̄ . 2̄ . 1̄ . :|
1 . . . 3 . . . 3 . . . 3 . . . 2 . . . 2 . . . 2 . . . 2 . . . :|
```

**System 3**

```
3 . 3 5 5 . 5 . 1̄ . 5 . 2̄ 2̄ 1̄ . . . 5 5 . . 5 . 2̄ . 2̄ . 1̄ . 5 .
1 . . . 3 . . . 3 . . . 3 . . . 2 . . . 2 . . . 2 . . . 2 . . .
```

**System 4**

```
3 . 3 5 5 . 5 . 1̄ . 5 . 1̄ 1̄ 5 . . . 5 5 . . 5 . 2̄ . 2̄ . 2̄ 1̄ . . :|
1 . . . 3 . . . 3 . . . 3 . . . 2 . . . 2 . . . 2 . . . 2 . . . :|
```

**System 5**

```
. . . 5 . . 5 . . . 5 . 1̄ . . 5 . . . 5 . . 5 . 2̄ . 2̄ . 2̄ 1̄ . .
1 . . . 3 . . . 3 . . . 3 . . . 2 . . . 2 . . . 2 . . . 2 . . .
```

**System 6**

```
. . . 5 . . 5 . . . 5 . 1̄ . 5 . . . . 5 . . 5 . 2̄ . 2̄ . 2̄ 1̄ . . :|
1 . 3 . 3 . . . 3 . . . 3 . . . 2 . . . 2 . . . 2 . . . 2 . . . :|
```

## SIMPLE TOMEYIELU

```
. . . . . . 3̄ . 1̄ . 2̄ . 4 . 4 . . . . . . . 3̄ . 1̄ . 2̄ . 1̄ . 1̄ .
2 . 1 . 3 . . . 3 . 1 . 2 . . . 2 . 1 . 3 . . . 3 . 1 . 3 . . .

. . . . 2̄ . 2̄ . 2̄ . 4 . 1̄ . 1̄ . . . . . . . 2̄ . 4 . 1̄ . 4 . 4 . :|
3 . 1 . 2 . . . 2 . 1 . 3 . . . 3 . 1 . 2 . . . 2 . 1 . 2 . . . :|

. . . . . . 3̄ 3̄ 1̄ . . 1̄ 4 . 4 . . . . . . . 3̄ 3̄ 1̄ . . 2̄ 1̄ . 1̄ .
2 . 1 . 3 . . . 3 . 1 . 2 . . . 2 . 1 . 3 . . . 3 . 1 . 3 . . .

. . . . 2̄ 2̄ . 2̄ . 4 . 1̄ . 1̄ . . . . . . . 2̄ . 2̄ . . 1̄ 4 . 4 . :|
3 . 1 . 2 . . . 2 . 1 . 3 . . . 3 . 1 . 2 . . . 2 . 1 . 2 . . . :|

. . . . . . 3̄ 3̄ . 1̄ . 1̄ 4 . 4 . . . . . . . 3̄ 3̄ . 1̄ . 2̄ 1̄ . 1̄ .
2 . 1 . 3 . . . 3 . 1 . 2 . . . 2 . 1 . 3 . . . 3 . 1 . 3 . . .

. . . . 2̄ 2̄ . 2̄ 4 . 4 1̄ . 1̄ . . . . . . . 2̄ . 2̄ 4 . 1̄ 4 . 4 . :|
3 . 1 . 2 . . . 2 . 1 . 3 . . . 3 . 1 . 2 . . . 2 . 1 . 2 . . . :|

. . . . . . 3̄ . 1̄ . 2̄ 4 . 4 . . . . . . . 3̄ . 1̄ . 2̄ 1̄ . 1̄ .
2 . 1 . 3 . . . 3 . 1 . 2 . . . 2 . 1 . 3 . . . 3 . 1 . 3 . . .

. . . . 2̄ 2̄ . 2̄ . 4 . 4 1̄ . 1̄ . . . . . . . 2̄ . 4 . 1̄ 4 . 4 . :|
3 . 1 . 2 . . . 2 . 1 . 3 . . . 3 . 1 . 2 . . . 2 . 1 . 2 . . . :|
```

# Chapter Five

## Transcriptions of Xylophone Music

**I**n making these transcriptions I have had to make a number of decisions regarding the presentation and the degree of accuracy I try to show. These decisions, and the reasons for them, are set out below.

The transcriptions show what I was taught by Joseph Kobom, but they are not precise bar-by-bar transcriptions of any specific performance. No two performances of a piece are ever the same. The basic pattern has a number of fairly standard variations but these may differ in detail between performances. The different variations may also be played in almost any order and repeated the number of times that the performer wishes. These variations, and the basic pattern have been printed with repeat signs at either end of the unit. In some pieces there is a "bridge" section which links from one part of the piece to another; these are played only once between each section and have been written without repeat signs. A piece can be ended at any point, often, as on the tape, by getting as quiet as possible, then just stopping.

Since the pitch of xylophones is not totally fixed and a performer may choose to start a piece on a different note which is adopted as the "tonic," the pieces have all been written out with C as tonic. The pitches used correspond to the western pentatonic scale, and should not be taken as an accurate indication of the actual pitch on the *gyil*, although I consider that they do represent the nearest available note in the western system. I decided to use western staff notation rather than any other because it is so familiar to musicians and music educators, and the learning of another system other than that and TUBS might take some time and be rather a negative stimulus to exploring this unfamiliar music.

On some occasions the notated rhythm is slightly inaccurate (such as bar 2 of *Ya ya kole zele*, where the left hand quarter note/eighth note motif should probably be notated as triplet half note/quarter note) but I considered that this would be much more complex to read, and also Joseph Kobom, when teaching the piece at a slow tempo, would play it as written, the "inaccuracy" occurring when it was played at speed. Notes are given different durations mainly for convenience of reading; they will all sound the same length except when the same note is played twice in rapid succession. Bar lines and time signatures are fairly arbitrary and are for convenience of reading rather than an accurate indication of stress and meter. All the pieces notated in 3/4 time can also be felt in 6/8. In order to keep the notation as simple as possible, most of the pieces have been written in quarter notes and eighth notes using a very fast pulse, usually 230-250 quarter note beats per minute. In *Tomeyielu* and *Kpawma pogmole ben Tuoper* slash note-heads on the middle line indicates the playing of the top bar with the handle of the beater. Following the staff notation the same pieces are presented in the same order using TUBS notation.

The transcriptions are as follows:

**Derkpee**
Funeral music "for brave warriors" from the Dagaare area.
**Kolaperbir**
"Cat and Mouse" — a recreational piece. Legend has it that the cat and mouse could never agree, so departed for separate parts of the forest. The mouse found somewhere with plenty of water and good food and prospered, but the cat found neither and became thin and weak. One day the cat was lying asleep under a tree. Its mouth was wide open from thirst and was full of flies. The mouse crept in unnoticed and bit the cat, the wound festered and the cat died. The moral is never to pick on someone who is smaller or weaker than you — they may be stronger than you think! The two parts of the music chase each other round like the cat and the mouse, especially in the last variation.
**Tomeyielu**
A work song "for building houses."
**Kurkurgambieyima**
"Man has gone out" — another funeral piece.

**Kpawma pogmole ben Tuoper**

"You can get beautiful girls in Tuoper market" — a traditional tune, much played by male xylophone players, extolling the virtues of the girls that can be found in Tuoper market.

**Bobodgilaso tingnebanena**

Recreational music using highlife rhythms. It dates from the internal wars in Burkina Faso (1960's –1970's) when it was usually played in pitou (locally distilled spirit) bars.

**Kpanlogo**

Kpanlogo is a traditional Ghanaian drum rhythm from which Highlife is partly derived.

**Highlife**

Highlife is the traditional Ghanaian popular music. This is a composition by Joseph Kobom using the rhythm pattern of the music.

**Sisaala Harvest Music**

Also known as the Gola gi dance. Traditionally performed in the Sisaala area of northern Ghana at the conclusion of harvest.

**Ya ya kole zele**

"Keep on begging!" — a recreational piece addressed to a lover to encourage them to keep up their attentions in the hope that you might finally weaken.

# Derkpee

# Kolaperbir

# Tomeyielu

**Bass Part**

**Both Parts Combined**

# Kurkurganbi eyima

# Kpawma Pogmole Ben Tuoper

# Bobodgilaso Tingnebanena

**13**

**16**

**19**

**22**

# Kpanlogo

**13**

**17**

**21**

# Highlife

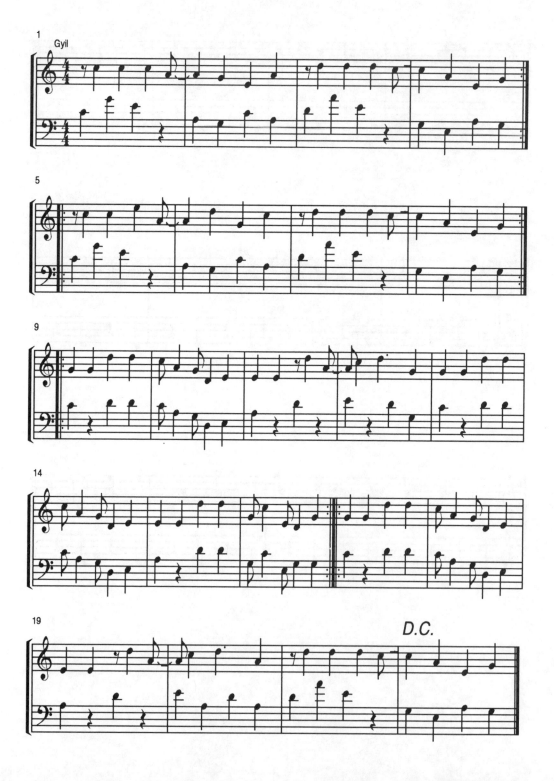

# Sisaala Harvest Music

# Ya Ya Kole Zele

## DERKPEE

**System 1**

```
.  1̄  .  .  5  .  5̲  .  5̲  .  5̲  .  .  5  .  .  4  .  1  .  1  .  1  .  :|
4  .  .  3  .  .  3̲  .  .  3̲  .  .  3  .  .  3  .  .  4̲  .  .  4̲  .  .  :|
```

**System 2**

```
.  1̄  1̄  .  5  .  5̲  .  5̲  .  5̲  .  .  5  5  .  4  .  1  .  1  .  1  .  :|
4  .  .  3  .  .  3̲  .  .  3̲  .  .  3  .  .  3  .  .  4̲  .  .  4̲  .  .  :|
```

**System 3**

```
.  1̄  .  .  5  .  2̄  .  5̲  .  5̲  .  .  5  .  .  4  .  1̄  .  1  .  1  .  :|
4  .  .  3  .  .  3̲  .  .  3̲  .  .  3  .  .  3  .  .  4̲  .  .  4̲  .  .  :|
```

**System 4**

```
.  1̄  .  .  5  .  5̲  .  1  .  5̲  .  .  5  .  .  4  .  1  .  3  .  1  .  :|
4  .  .  3  .  .  3̲  .  .  3̲  .  .  3  .  .  3  .  .  4̲  .  .  4̲  .  .  :|
```

**System 5**

```
.  1̄  .  .  5  .  5̲  .  5̲  .  5̲  5  .  5  .  .  4  .  1  .  1  .  1  1̄  :|
4  .  .  3  .  .  3  .  .  3  .  .  3  .  .  3  .  .  4  .  .  4  .  .  :|
```

## KOLAPERBIR

## TOMEYIELU

```
. . . . . . 3̄ . 1̄ . 2̄ 4 . 4 . . . . . . . . 3̄ . 1̄ . 2̄ 1̄ . 1̄ .
2 . 1 . 3 . . . 3 . 1 . 2 . . . 2 . 1 . 3 . . . 3 . 1 . 3 . . .
```

```
. . . . 2̄ 2̄ . 2̄ . 4 4 1̄ . 1̄ . . . . . . . . 2̄ . 4 . 1̄ 4 . 4 . ‖:
3 . 1 . 2 . . . 2 . 1 3 . . . 3 . 1 . 2 . . . 2 . 1 . 2 . . . :‖
```

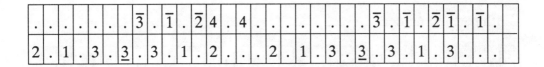

```
. . . . . . . 3̄ . 1̄ . 2̄ 4 . 4 . . . . . . . 3̄ . 1̄ . 2̄ 1̄ . 1̄ .
2 . 1 . 3 . 3̲ . 3 . 1 . 2 . . . 2 . 1 . 3 . 3̲ . 3 . 1 . 3 . . .
```

```
. . . . 2̄ 2̄ . 2̄ . 4 . 4 1̄ . 1̄ . . . . . . . . 2̄ . 4 . 1̄ 4 . 4 . ‖:
3 . 1 . 2 . 2̲ . 2 . 1 . 3 . . . 3 . 1 . 2 . 2̲ . 2 . 1 . 2 . . . :‖
```

Bass part

```
2 . . 1 3 . . . 3 . . 1 2 . . . 2 . . 1 3 . . . 3 . . 1 3 . . .
. 4̲ . . . . . 3̲ . . 3̲ . . . . 4̲ . . 4̲ . . . . 3̲ . . 3̲ . . . . 3̲ .
```

```
3 . . 1 2 . . . 2 . . 1 3 . . . 3 . . 1 2 . . . 2 . . 1 2 . . . ‖:
. 3̲ . . . . 4̲ . . 4̲ . . . . 3̲ . . 3̲ . . . . 4̲ . . 4̲ . . . . 4̲ . :‖
```

## TOMEYIELU, continued

```
| 2 . . | 1 3 . | . . 3 | . . 1 | 2 . . | . 2 . | . 1 3 | . . . | 3 . . | 1 3 . | . . |
| . 4 . | . . . | 3 . . | 3 . . | . . . | 2 . . | 4 . . | . . 3 | . . 3 | . . . | . 3 . |
```

```
| 3 . . | 1 2 . | . . 2 | . . 1 | 3 . . | . 3 . | . 1 2 | . . . | 2 . . | 1 2 . | . . . | :|
| . 3 . | . . . | 2 . . | 4 . . | . . . | 3 . . | 3 . . | . . 2 | . . 4 | . . . | . 4 . | :|
```

## Both parts combined

```
| 2 2 . | 1 3 3 | . 3̄ . | 1̄ . 2̄ | 4 . 4 | . 2 2 | . 1 3 3 | . 3̄ . | 1̄ . 2̄ | 1̄ . 1̄ . |
| 2̲ . 4̲ | . 3̲ . | 1 . 3 | . 1 . | 2 . . | . 2̲ . | 4̲ . 3̲ | . 1 . | 3 . 1 | . 3 . . . |
```

```
| 3 3 . | 1 2 2 | . 2̄ . | 4 . 4 | 3̄ . 1̄ | . 3 3 | . 1 2 2 | . 2̄ . | 4 . 1̄ | 4 . 4 . | :|
| 3̲ . 5̲ | . 2̲ . | 4̲ . 2 | . 1 . | 3 . . | . 3̲ . | 5̲ . 2̲ | . 4̲ . | 2 . 1 | . 2 . . . | :|
```

```
| . . . x | . . x . | . x x . | . x . . | x . . x | . . x . | . x . . | x . . x | x . . x . |
| 2 . 1 . | 3 . 3̲ . | 3 . 1 . | 2 . . . | 2 . 1 . | 3 . 3̲ . | 3 . 1 . | 3 . . . |
```

```
| . x . . | x . . x | . . x x | . . x . | . x . . | x . . x | . . x . | . x x . | . . . . | :|
| 3 . 1 . | 2 . 2̲ . | 2 . 1 . | 3 . . . | 3 . 1 . | 2 . 2̲ . | 2 . 1 . | 2 . . . | :|
```

## KURKURGANBIEYIMA

| 4 | $\bar{1}$ | . | $\bar{1}$ | . | . | 4 2 | . | . | . | . | 4 5 | . | 5 | . | . | 4 | . | . | . | . | . | :\| |
|---|---|---|---|---|---|---|---|---|---|---|---|---|---|---|---|---|---|---|---|---|---|---|
| . | . | . | 1 | . | 1 | . | . | $\underline{5}$ | . | 2 | . | . | . | . | $\underline{5}$ | . | 2 | . | 1 | . | . | 1 . :\| |

| 4 | $\bar{1}$ | . | $\bar{1}$ | . | . | 4 5 | . | 1 5 | . | 4 5 | . | 5 | . | . | 4 | . | . | . | . | . | :\| |
|---|---|---|---|---|---|---|---|---|---|---|---|---|---|---|---|---|---|---|---|---|---|
| . | . | . | 1 | . | 1 | . | . | $\underline{5}$ | . | 2 | . | . | . | . | $\underline{5}$ | . | 2 | . | 1 | . | . 1 . :\| |

| 4 | $\bar{1}$ | . | $\bar{1}$ | . | . | 4 5 | . | 5 | . | 5 4 5 | . | 5 | . | . | 4 | . | . | . | . | . | :\| |
|---|---|---|---|---|---|---|---|---|---|---|---|---|---|---|---|---|---|---|---|---|---|
| . | . | . | 1 | . | 1 | . | . | $\underline{5}$ | . | 2 | . | . | . | . | $\underline{5}$ | . | 2 | . | 1 | . | . 1 . :\| |

| 4 | $\bar{1}$ | . | $\bar{1}$ | . | . | 5 $\bar{2}$ | . | 5 | . | $\bar{1}$ 4 5 | . | 5 | . | . | 4 | . | . | . | . | . | :\| |
|---|---|---|---|---|---|---|---|---|---|---|---|---|---|---|---|---|---|---|---|---|---|
| . | . | . | 1 | . | 1 | . | . | $\underline{5}$ | . | 2 | . | . | . | . | $\underline{5}$ | . | 2 | . | 1 | . | . 1 . :\| |

| 4 | $\bar{1}$ | . | $\bar{1}$ | . | . | 5 $\bar{3}$ | . | $\bar{2}$ | . | $\bar{1}$ 4 5 | . | $\bar{1}$ | . | . | 4 | . | . | . | . | . | :\| |
|---|---|---|---|---|---|---|---|---|---|---|---|---|---|---|---|---|---|---|---|---|---|
| . | . | . | 1 | . | 1 | . | . | $\underline{5}$ | . | 2 | . | . | . | . | $\underline{5}$ | . | 2 | . | 1 | . | . 1 . :\| |

| 4 | $\bar{1}$ | . | $\bar{1}$ | . | . | 5 $\bar{3}$ | . | $\bar{2}$ | . | $\bar{1}$ 4 5 | . | $\bar{1}$ | . | . | 4 | . | . | . | . | . | :\| |
|---|---|---|---|---|---|---|---|---|---|---|---|---|---|---|---|---|---|---|---|---|---|
| . | . | . | $\underline{4}$ | . | 1 | . | . | $\underline{5}$ | . | 2 | . | . | . | . | $\underline{4}$ | . | 2 | . | 1 | . | . 1 . :\| |

## KPAWMA POGMOLE BEN TUOPER

| | | | | | | | | | | | | | | | | | | | | | | | |
|---|---|---|---|---|---|---|---|---|---|---|---|---|---|---|---|---|---|---|---|---|---|---|---|
| . | . | . | . | . | . | . | . | . | . | . | . | . | . | . | . | . | . | . | . | . | . | . | ǀ |
| 3̲ | . | 5̲ | . | 3̲ | . | 5̲ | . | 3̲ | . | 2̲ | . | 3̲ | . | 5̲ | . | 3̲ | . | 5̲ | . | 3̲ | . | 2̲ | . | ǀ |

| | | | | | | | | | | | | | | | | | | | | | | | |
|---|---|---|---|---|---|---|---|---|---|---|---|---|---|---|---|---|---|---|---|---|---|---|---|
| . | . | 4 | . | . | 4 | . | . | . | . | 4 | . | 4 | 5 | . | 4 | . | 3 | 3 | . | 2 | . | . | . |
| 4̲ | . | 1 | . | 4̲ | . | 1 | . | 4̲ | . | 2̲ | . | 3̲ | . | 5̲ | . | 3̲ | . | 5̲ | . | 3̲ | . | 2̲ | . |

| | | | | | | | | | | | | | | | | | | | | | | | |
|---|---|---|---|---|---|---|---|---|---|---|---|---|---|---|---|---|---|---|---|---|---|---|---|
| . | . | 1 | . | . | 1 | . | . | . | . | . | . | . | . | . | . | . | . | . | . | . | . | . | . |
| 4̲ | . | 1 | . | 4̲ | . | 1 | . | 4̲ | . | 2̲ | . | 4̲ | . | 1 | . | 4̲ | . | 1 | . | 4̲ | . | 2̲ | . |

| | | | | | | | | | | | | | | | | | | | | | | | |
|---|---|---|---|---|---|---|---|---|---|---|---|---|---|---|---|---|---|---|---|---|---|---|---|
| . | . | 5 | . | . | 5 | . | . | . | . | 5 | . | 5 | 1̄ | . | 5 | . | 4 | 4 | . | 3 | . | . | . |
| 3̲ | . | 5̲ | . | 3̲ | . | 5̲ | . | 3̲ | . | 2̲ | . | 4̲ | . | 1 | . | 4̲ | . | 1 | . | 4̲ | . | 2̲ | . |

| | | | | | | | | | | | | | | | | | | | | | | | |
|---|---|---|---|---|---|---|---|---|---|---|---|---|---|---|---|---|---|---|---|---|---|---|---|
| . | . | 3 | . | . | 3 | . | . | . | . | . | . | . | . | . | . | . | . | . | . | . | . | . | :ǀ |
| 3̲ | . | 5̲ | . | 3̲ | . | 5̲ | . | 3̲ | . | 2̲ | . | 3̲ | . | 5̲ | . | 3̲ | . | 5̲ | . | 3̲ | . | 2̲ | . | :ǀ |

| | | | | | | | | | | | | | | | | | | | | | | | |
|---|---|---|---|---|---|---|---|---|---|---|---|---|---|---|---|---|---|---|---|---|---|---|---|
| . | . | 4 | . | . | 4 | . | . | . | . | 4 | . | 4 | 5 | . | 4 | . | 3 | 3 | . | 2 | . | . | . |
| 4̲ | . | 1 | . | 4̲ | . | 1 | . | 4̲ | . | 2̲ | . | 3̲ | . | 5̲ | . | 3̲ | . | 5̲ | . | 3̲ | . | 2̲ | . |

| | | | | | | | | | | | | | | | | | | | | | | | |
|---|---|---|---|---|---|---|---|---|---|---|---|---|---|---|---|---|---|---|---|---|---|---|---|
| . | . | 1̄ | . | . | 1̄ | . | . | . | . | 1̄ | . | 1̄ | 2̄ | . | 1̄ | . | 5 | 5 | . | 4 | . | . | . |
| 4̲ | . | 1 | . | 4̲ | . | 1 | . | 4̲ | . | 2̲ | . | 4̲ | . | 1 | . | 4̲ | . | 1 | . | 4̲ | . | 2̲ | . |

## KPAWMA POGMOLE BEN TUOPER, continued

## BOBODGILASO TINGNEBANENA

| 1̄ | . | 3̄ | . | 2̄ | . | 3̄ | . | . | 5 | . | 5 | . | 4 | . | . | 1̄ | . | 1̄ | . | 2̄ | . | 3̄ | . | . | 5 | . | 5 | . | 4 | . | . | :‖ |
| 1 | . | 3 | . | 2 | . | 3 | . | 5̲ | . | 3 | . | . | . | 3 | . | 1 | . | 3 | . | 2 | . | 3 | . | 5̲ | . | 3 | . | . | . | 3 | . | :‖ |

| . | 1 | . | 3 2 | . | 3 | . | . | 5 | . | 4 | . | 5 | . | . | . | 1 | . | 3 2 | . | 3 | . | . | 5 | . | 5 | . | 4 | . | . | :‖ |
| 4̲ | . | 3̲ | . | 5̲ | . | 3̲ | . | 5̲ | . | 3 | . | . | . | 3 | . | 4̲ | . | 3̲ | . | 5̲ | . | 3̲ | . | 5̲ | . | 3 | . | . | . | 3 | . | :‖ |

| . | 1̄ 3̄ | . | 2̄ | . | 1̄ | . | 5 5 | . | 5 | . | 4 | . | . | . | 1̄ 1̄ | . | 2̄ | . | 3̄ | . | 1̄ 5 | . | 4 | . | 5 | . | . | :‖ |
| 1 | . | 3 | . | 2 | . | 3 | . | 5̲ | . | 3 | . | . | . | 3 | . | 1 | . | 3 | . | 2 | . | 3 | . | 5̲ | . | 3 | . | . | . | 3 | . | :‖ |

| . | 1̄ | . | 2̄ | . | 1̄ | . | 5 | . | 5 | . | 5 | . | 4 | . | . | . | 1̄ | . | 2̄ | . | 1̄ | . | 5 | . | 5 | . | 4 | . | 5 | . | . | :‖ |
| 1 | . | 3 | . | 2 | . | 3 | . | 5̲ | . | 3 | . | . | . | 3 | . | 1 | . | 3 | . | 2 | . | 3 | . | 5̲ | . | 3 | . | . | . | 3 | . | :‖ |

| . | 1̄ 3̄ | . | 2̄ 3̄ | . | 2̄ 5 5 | . | 5 | . | 4 | . | . | . | 1̄ 1̄ | . | 2̄ 2̄ | . | 1̄ 5 5 | . | 5 | . | 4 | . | . | :‖ |
| 1 | . | 3 | . | 2 | . | 3 | . | 5̲ | . | 3 | . | . | . | 3 | . | 1 | . | 3 | . | 2 | . | 3 | . | 5̲ | . | 3 | . | . | . | 3 | . | :‖ |

| . | 1̄ 1̄ | . | 3̄ 3̄ | . | 2̄ | . | 5 | . | 5 | . | 4 | . | . | . | 1̄ 3̄ | . | 2̄ 4̄ | . | 3̄ | . | 5 | . | 5 | . | 4 | . | . | :‖ |
| 1 | . | 3 | . | 2 | . | 3 | . | 5̲ | . | 3 | . | . | . | 3 | . | 1 | . | 3 | . | 2 | . | 3 | . | 5̲ | . | 3 | . | . | . | 3 | . | :‖ |

## KPANLOGO

Line 1:
`. . . 5 . . 5 . . . 5 . 1̄ . . 5 . . . 5 . . 5 . 2̄ . 5 . 2̄ . 5 .`
`3 . . . 3 . . . 3 . . . 3 . . . 2 . . . 2 . . . 2 . . . 2 . . .`

Line 2:
`3 . 3 5 . . 5 . . . 5 . 1̄ . 5 . . . . 5 . . 5 . 2̄ . 2̄ . 2̄ 1̄ . 5 :|`
`1 . . . 3 . . . 3 . . . 3 . . . 2 . . . 2 . . . 2 . . . 2 . . . :|`

Line 3:
`3 . 3 5 . . 5 . 1̄ . 5 . 1̄ 2̄ . 5 . . . 5 . . 5 . 2̄ . 2̄ . 2̄ 1̄ . 5`
`1 . . . 3 . . . 3 . . . 3 . . . 2 . . . 2 . . . 2 . . . 2 . . .`

Line 4:
`3 . 3 5 . . 5 . 1̄ . 5 . 1̄ 2̄ . 1̄ . . . 5 . . 5 . 2̄ . 2̄ . 2̄ 1̄ . . :|`
`1 . . . 3 . . . 3 . . . 3 . . . 2 . . . 2 . . . 2 . . . 2 . . . :|`

Line 5:
`. 3 . 5 . . 5 . . . 5 . 1̄ . . 5 . . . 5 . . 5 . 3̄ . 3̄ . 3̄ 2̄ . 1̄`
`1 . 3 . 3 . . . 3 . . . 3 . . . 2 . . . 2 . . . 2 . . . 2 . . .`

Line 6:
`. 3 . 5 . . 5 . . . 5 . 1̄ . 5 . . . . 5 . . 5 . 3̄ . 3̄ . 3̄ 2̄ . 1̄ :|`
`1 . 3 . 3 . . . 3 . . . 3 . . . 2 . . . 2 . . . 2 . . . 2 . . . :|`

## HIGHLIFE

### First part

$.\ \bar{1}\ .\ \bar{1}\ .\ \bar{1}\ .\ 5\ .\ .\ 4\ .\ 3\ .\ 5\ .\ .\ \bar{2}\ .\ \bar{2}\ .\ \bar{2}\ .\ \bar{1}\ .\ .\ 5\ .\ 3\ .\ 4\ .\ \;:|$
$1\ .\ 4\ .\ 3\ .\ .\ .\ \underline{5}\ .\ \underline{4}\ .\ 1\ .\ \underline{5}\ .\ 2\ .\ 5\ .\ 3\ .\ .\ .\ \underline{4}\ .\ \underline{3}\ .\ \underline{5}\ .\ \underline{4}\ .\ \;:|$

$.\ \bar{1}\ .\ \bar{1}\ .\ \bar{3}\ .\ 5\ .\ .\ \bar{2}\ .\ 4\ .\ \bar{1}\ .\ .\ \bar{2}\ .\ \bar{2}\ .\ \bar{2}\ .\ \bar{1}\ .\ .\ 5\ .\ 3\ .\ 4\ .\ \;:|$
$1\ .\ 4\ .\ 3\ .\ .\ .\ \underline{5}\ .\ \underline{4}\ .\ 1\ .\ \underline{5}\ .\ 2\ .\ 5\ .\ 3\ .\ .\ .\ \underline{4}\ .\ \underline{3}\ .\ \underline{5}\ .\ \underline{4}\ .\ \;:|$

### Second part

$4\ .\ 4\ .\ \bar{2}\ .\ \bar{2}\ .\ \bar{1}\ 5\ .\ 4\ 2\ .\ 3\ .\ 3\ .\ 3\ .\ .\ \bar{2}\ .\ 5\ .\ \bar{1}\ .\ \bar{2}\ .\ .\ 4\ .$
$1\ .\ .\ .\ 2\ .\ 2\ .\ 1\ \underline{5}\ .\ \underline{4}\ 2\ .\ \underline{3}\ .\ \underline{5}\ .\ .\ .\ 2\ .\ .\ .\ 3\ .\ .\ .\ 2\ .\ \underline{4}\ .$

$4\ .\ 4\ .\ \bar{2}\ .\ \bar{2}\ .\ \bar{1}\ 5\ .\ 4\ 2\ .\ 3\ .\ 3\ .\ 3\ .\ \bar{2}\ .\ \bar{2}\ .\ 4\ \bar{1}\ .\ 3\ 2\ .\ 4\ .\ \;:|$
$1\ .\ .\ .\ 2\ .\ 2\ .\ 1\ \underline{5}\ .\ \underline{4}\ 2\ .\ \underline{3}\ .\ \underline{5}\ .\ .\ .\ 2\ .\ 2\ .\ \underline{4}\ 1\ .\ \underline{3}\ \underline{4}\ .\ \underline{4}\ .\ \;:|$

### Link back to first part

$4\ .\ 4\ .\ \bar{2}\ .\ \bar{2}\ .\ \bar{1}\ 5\ .\ 4\ 2\ .\ 3\ .\ 3\ .\ 3\ .\ .\ \bar{2}\ .\ 5\ .\ \bar{1}\ .\ \bar{2}\ .\ .\ 5\ .$
$1\ .\ .\ .\ 2\ .\ 2\ .\ 1\ \underline{5}\ .\ \underline{4}\ 2\ .\ \underline{3}\ .\ \underline{5}\ .\ .\ .\ 2\ .\ .\ .\ 3\ .\ \underline{5}\ .\ 2\ .\ \underline{5}\ .$

$.\ \bar{2}\ .\ \bar{2}\ .\ \bar{2}\ .\ \bar{1}\ .\ .\ 5\ .\ 3\ .\ 4\ .\ \;|$
$2\ .\ 5\ .\ 3\ .\ .\ .\ \underline{4}\ .\ \underline{3}\ .\ \underline{5}\ .\ \underline{4}\ .\ \;|$

## SISAALA HARVEST MUSIC

**Introduction**

| 4 | . | 3 | . | 5 | . | $\bar{2}$ | . | $\bar{1}$ | . | $\bar{2}$ | . | . | $\bar{2}$ | . | . | $\bar{2}$ | . | 5 | . | 3 | . | $\bar{2}$ | . | . | $\bar{2}$ | . | . | $\bar{2}$ | . | 4 | . | 3 | . | ❘ |

| $\underline{4}$ | . | $\underline{3}$ | . | $\underline{5}$ | . | $\underline{4}$ | . | 1 | . | $\underline{5}$ | . | 1 | . | 2 | . | . | . | $\underline{3}$ | . | $\underline{5}$ | . | $\underline{4}$ | . | 1 | . | 3 | . | . | . | $\underline{4}$ | . | 1 | . | ❘ |

**Part 1**

| $\bar{2}$ | . | . | $\bar{2}$ | . | . | $\bar{2}$ | . | 4 | . | 3 | . | $\bar{2}$ | . | . | $\bar{2}$ | . | . | $\bar{2}$ | . | 5 | . | 3 | . |
| $\underline{5}$ | . | 2 | . | 3 | . | . | . | $\underline{4}$ | . | 1 | . | $\underline{5}$ | . | 2 | . | 3 | . | . | . | $\underline{3}$ | . | $\underline{5}$ | . |

| $\bar{3}$ | . | . | $\bar{3}$ | . | . | $\bar{3}$ | . | 4 | . | 3 | . | $\bar{2}$ | . | . | $\bar{2}$ | . | . | $\bar{2}$ | . | 5 | . | 3 | . |
| $\underline{4}$ | . | 1 | . | 3 | . | . | . | $\underline{4}$ | . | 1 | . | $\underline{5}$ | . | 2 | . | 3 | . | . | . | $\underline{3}$ | . | $\underline{5}$ | . |

| $\bar{3}$ | . | . | $\bar{3}$ | . | . | $\bar{3}$ | . | $\bar{1}$ | . | 3 | . | $\bar{3}$ | . | . | $\bar{3}$ | . | . | $\bar{3}$ | . | . | $\bar{1}$ | . | . |
| $\underline{4}$ | . | 1 | . | 3 | . | . | . | $\underline{3}$ | . | $\underline{5}$ | . | $\underline{4}$ | . | 1 | . | 3 | . | . | . | 4 | . | 3 | . |

| $\bar{2}$ | . | . | $\bar{2}$ | . | . | $\bar{2}$ | . | 5 | . | 2 | . | 4 | . | $\bar{1}$ | . | 3 | . | 5 | . | $\bar{2}$ | . | $\bar{1}$ | . | :❘ |
| $\underline{5}$ | . | 2 | . | 3 | . | . | . | $\underline{5}$ | . | $\underline{2}$ | . | $\underline{4}$ | . | 1 | . | $\underline{3}$ | . | $\underline{5}$ | . | $\underline{4}$ | . | 1 | . | :❘ |

**Part 2**

| $\bar{2}$ | . | . | $\bar{2}$ | . | . | $\bar{2}$ | . | $\bar{3}$ | . | $\bar{1}$ | . | . | $\bar{2}$ | . | . | 5 | . | $\bar{1}$ | . | $\bar{2}$ | . | 5 | . |
| $\underline{5}$ | . | 2 | . | 3 | . | . | . | 4 | . | 3 | . | 5 | . | 2 | . | 3 | . | 2 | . | 5 | . | 3 | . |

| $\bar{3}$ | . | . | $\bar{3}$ | . | . | $\bar{3}$ | . | 4 | . | 3 | . | $\bar{2}$ | . | . | $\bar{2}$ | . | . | $\bar{2}$ | . | 5 | . | 3 | . |
| 4 | . | 1 | . | 3 | . | . | . | $\underline{4}$ | . | 1 | . | $\underline{5}$ | . | 2 | . | 3 | . | . | . | $\underline{3}$ | . | $\underline{5}$ | . |

| $\bar{3}$ | . | . | $\bar{3}$ | . | . | $\bar{3}$ | . | 4 | . | 3 | . | $\bar{3}$ | . | . | $\bar{3}$ | . | . | $\bar{3}$ | . | . | $\bar{1}$ | . | $\bar{1}$ |
| $\underline{4}$ | . | 1 | . | 3 | . | . | . | $\underline{3}$ | . | $\underline{5}$ | . | $\underline{4}$ | . | 1 | . | 3 | . | . | . | 4 | . | 3 | . |

| $\bar{2}$ | . | . | $\bar{2}$ | . | . | $\bar{2}$ | . | 5 | . | 2 | . | 4 | . | $\bar{1}$ | . | 3 | . | 5 | . | $\bar{2}$ | . | $\bar{1}$ | . | :❘ |
| $\underline{5}$ | . | 2 | . | 3 | . | . | . | $\underline{5}$ | . | $\underline{2}$ | . | $\underline{4}$ | . | 1 | . | $\underline{3}$ | . | $\underline{5}$ | . | $\underline{4}$ | . | 1 | . | :❘ |

## SISAALA HARVEST MUSIC, continued

**Part 3**

```
2̄ . . 2̄ . . 2̄ . 3̄ . 1̄ . . 2̄ . . 5 . 1̄ . 2̄ . 5 .
5̲ . 2 . 3 . . . 4 . 3 . 5 . 2 . 3 . 2 . 5 . 3 .

3̄ . . 3̄ . . 3̄ . 4 . 3 . 2̄ . . 2̄ . . 2̄ . 5 . 3 .
4 . 1 . 3 . . . 4̲ . 1 . 5̲ . 2 . 3 . . . 3̲ . 5̲ .

3̄ . . 3̄ . . 3̄ . 4 . 3 . 3̄ . . 3̄ . . 3̄ . . 1̄ . 1̄
4̲ . 1 . 3 . . . 3̲ . 5̲ . 4̲ . 1 . 3 . . . 4 . 3 .

2̄ . . 3̄ . . 2̄ . . 3̄ . . 2̄ . . 3̄ . . 2̄ . . 1̄ . .
5 . 2 . 3 . . . 5 . 3 . 4 . 1 . 3 . . . 4 . 3 .

2̄ . . 3̄ . . 2̄ . . 3̄ . . 2̄ . . 3̄ . . 2̄ . . 5 . . |
5 . 2 . 3 . . . 5 . 3 . 5 . 2 . 3 . . . 5 . 3 . |
```

**Part 4**

```
3̄ . . 3̄ . . 3̄ . . 3̄ . . 3̄ . . 3̄ . . 3̄ . . 3̄ . .
4 . 1 . 3 . . . 4 . 3 . 5 . 2 . 3 . . . 5 . 3 .

3̄ . . 3̄ . . 3̄ . . 3̄ . . 3̄ . . 3̄ . . 3̄ . . 1̄ . 1̄
4 . 1 . 3 . . . 4 . 3 . 4 . 1 . 3 . . . 4 . 3 .

2̄ . . 2̄ . . 2̄ . . 2̄ . . 2̄ . . 3̄ . . 2̄ . . 1̄ . 3̄
5 . 2 . 3 . . . 5 . 3 . 4 . 1 . 3 . . . 4 . 2 .

2̄ . . 3̄ . . 2̄ . . 3̄ . . 2̄ . . 1̄ . . 5 . 1 . 3 .
5 . 2 . 3 . . . 5 . 3 . 5 . 2 . 3 . . . 4̲ . 3̲ .
```

## SISAALA HARVEST MUSIC, continued

| 3̄ | . | . | 3̄ | . | . | 3̄ | . | 1 | . | 3 | . | 5 | . | . | 5 | . | . | 5 | . | 1 | . | 3 | . |
| 4̲ | . | 1 | . | 3 | . | . | . | 4̲ | . | 3̲ | . | 5̲ | . | 2 | . | 3 | . | . | . | 4̲ | . | 3̲ | . |

| 3̄ | . | . | 3̄ | . | . | 3̄ | . | 1 | . | 3 | . | 3̄ | . | . | 2̄ | . | . | 1̄ | . | 1 | . | 3 | . |
| 4̲ | . | 1 | . | 3 | . | . | . | 4̲ | . | 3̲ | . | 4̲ | . | 1 | . | 3 | . | . | . | 4̲ | . | 3̲ | . |

| 2̄ | . | . | 1̄ | . | . | 5 | . | 2 | . | 3 | . | 1̄ | . | . | 2̄ | . | . | 1̄ | . | 1 | . | 3 | . |
| 5̲ | . | 2 | . | 3 | . | . | . | 4̲ | . | 3̲ | . | 4̲ | . | 1 | . | 3 | . | . | . | 4̲ | . | 3̲ | . |

| 5 | . | . | 1̄ | . | . | 5 | . | 2 | . | 3 | . | 5 | . | . | 1̄ | . | . | 5 | . | 2 | . | 3 | . | :\| |
| 5̲ | . | 2 | . | 3 | . | . | . | 4̲ | . | 3̲ | . | 5̲ | . | 2 | . | 3 | . | . | . | 4̲ | . | 3̲ | . | :\| |

| 5 | . | 2̄ | . | 1̄ | . |
| 5̲ | . | 4̲ | . | 1 | . |

Back to Part 1.

## YA YA KOLE ZELE

```
. . 2̄ . 2̄ . 2̄ . 5 . . . . . . . . 1̄ . 1̄ . 1̄ . 5 . . . . . . . . .
. . 5 . 2 . . . 3 . . 5̲ 2 . 4̲ 1 . . 4 . 2 . . . 3 . . 5̲ 2 . 4̲ 1 . .

1̄ . 1̄ . 1̄ . 4 . . . . 2 3 . 3 . 3 . . . . 4 4 . 1 . 1 . . 2 . . 5̲ .  :||
4 . 2 . . . 4̲ . . . 2̲ . 4̲ . 3̲ . 5̲ . . . 2 . . . . 4̲ . . . 2̲ . . 3̲ .  :||

. . 2̄ . 3̄ . 2̄ . 5 . . . . . . . . 1̄ . 2̄ . 1̄ . 5 . . . . . . . . .
. . 5 . 2 . . 2̲ . 3̲ . 5̲ 2 . 4̲ 1 . . 4 . 2 . . 2̲ . 3̲ . 5̲ 2 . 4̲ 1 . .

1̄ . 2̄ . 1̄ . 4 . . . . 2 3 . 3 . 3 . . . . 4 4 . 1 . 1 . . 2 . . 5̲ .  :||
4 . 2 . . . 4̲ . . . 2̲ . 4̲ . 3̲ . 5̲ . . . 2 . . . . 4̲ . . . 2̲ . . 3̲ .  :||

. 2̄ . 2̄ 3̄ . 2̄ . 5 5 . 5 . . . 1̄ . 1̄ 1̄ . 2̄ . 4 . 3 5 . 5 . . . 1̄ . 1̄
. . 5 . 2 . . . 3 . . 5̲ 2 . 4̲ 1 . . 4 . 2 . . . 3 . . 5̲ 2 . 4̲ 1 . .

1̄ . 2̄ . 1̄ . 4 . . . . 2 3 . 3 . 3 . . . . 4 4 . 1 . 1 . . 2 . . 5̲ .  :||
4 . 2 . . . 4̲ . . . 2̲ . 4̲ . 3̲ . 5̲ . . . 2 . . . . 4̲ . . . 2̲ . . 3̲ .  :||

. 2̄ . 2̄ 3̄ . 2̄ . 5 2̄ . 2̄ . . . 1̄ . 1̄ 1̄ . 5 . 4 . 3 5 . 5 . . . 1̄ . 2̄
. . 5 . 2 . . 2̲ . 3̲ . 5̲ 2 . 4̲ 1 . . 4 . 2 . . 2̲ . 3̲ . 5̲ 2 . 4̲ 1 . .

5 . 1̄ . 5 . 4 . . . . 2 3 . 3 . 3 . . . . 4 4 . 1 . 1 . . 2 . . 5̄ .  :||
4 . 2 . . . 4̲ . . . 2̲ . 4̲ . 3̲ . 5̲ . . . 2 . . . . 4̲ . . . 2̲ . . 3̲ .  :||
```

### Also available – THE PERFORMANCE IN WORLD MUSIC SERIES

*Drum Gahu: The Rhythms of West African Drumming.* David Locke. Book, $15.95. 90 minute study cassette, $14.95.

*Drum Damba: Talking Drum Lessons.* David Locke featuring Abubakari Lunna. Book, $17.95. 90 minute study cassette, $14.95. Performance video, $34.95. Stories and folklore video, $34.95.

*Kpegisu: A War Drum of the Ewe.* David Locke featuring Godwin Agbeli. Book, $19.95. Study cassette, $14.95. Documentary video, $99.95. Video master class, $79.95.

*Salsa!: The Rhythm of Latin Music.* Charley Gerard with Marty Sheller. Book, $14.95. Study cassette, $12.95.

*The Music of Santería: Traditional Rhythms of the Batá Drums.* John Amira and Steven Cornelius. Book, $19.95. Accompanying cassette, $12.95.

*The Drums of Vodou.* Lois Wilcken featuring Frisner Augustin. Book, $19.95. Accompanying tape, 12.95.

*Synagogue Song in America.* Joseph A. Levine. Book, $29.95. Three study tapes, $30.00.

ALSO – *The New Folk Music.* Craig Harris. Profiles of leading contemporary folk singer-songwriters and instrumentalists. Book, $19.95.

### WORLD MUSIC CASSETTES

*White Cliffs Media World Music/Folk Music Sampler.* Performers from the book *The New Folk Music* plus world music from other tapes below published by White Cliffs Media. $10.95.

*Xylophone Music from Ghana.* Virtuoso performances by Joseph Kobom. $12.95.

*The Music of Santería: The Oru del Igbodu.* John Amira. Landmark recording features performances of transcriptions from the book. $12.95.

*Abubakari Lunna: Virtuoso Drummer of Dagbon.* Magnificent talking drum percussion from Ghana's Abubakari Lunna. $12.95.

*Drum Gahu Field Tape.* Enlivening percussion festival music from the Ewe people of Ghana. $12.95.

*The Drums of Vodou.* Performances by Haitian drum master Frisner Augustin. From the book of the same name by Lois Wilcken. $12.95.

To order call 1-800-359-3210 with Visa, Mastercard or American Express. Or, add $2.50 for shipping and mail check to White Cliffs Media, P.O. Box 561, Crown Point, IN 46307.